Orange As a Pumpkin

Orange comme une citrouille

written by **Molly Dingles**

illustrated by **Walter Velez**

dingles&company New Jersey

For Peter

First printing

PUBLISHED BY dingles&company
P.O. Box 508 • Sea Girt, New Jersey • 08750
WEBSITE: www.dingles.com • E-MAIL: info@dingles.com

LIBRARY BINDING EDITION DISTRIBUTED BY **GUMDROP BOOKS**
P.O. Box 505 • Bethany, Missouri • 64424
(660) 425-7777

Library of Congress Catalog Card No.: 2004091384
ISBN: 1-891997-69-6

Printed in the United States of America

●

ART DIRECTED & DESIGNED BY Barbie Lambert

ENGLISH EDITED BY Andrea Curley
FRENCH EDITED BY Jonathan Strickland

EDUCATION CONSULTANT Kathleen P. Miller

PREPRESS BY Pixel Graphics, Inc.

Molly Dingles

is the author of *Jinka Jinka Jelly Bean* and *Little Lee Lee's Birthday Bang*. As Judy Zocchi, she has written the *Paulie & Sasha* series. She is a writer and lyricist who holds a bachelor's degree in fine arts/theater from Mount Saint Mary's College and a master's degree in educational theater from New York University. She lives in Manasquan, New Jersey, with her husband, David.

Walter Velez

was born in New York. He attended the High School of Art and Design and later the School of Visual Arts. He has done illustration work for many major book and gaming companies. He is known for the popular series *Thieves World* as well as the *Myth* series for Ace Books. He has also produced trading cards for *Goosebumps* and *Dune*. In addition, Walter has illustrated several *Star Wars* books for Random House. He lives in Queens, New York, with his wife, Kriti, and daughter, Kassandra.

The Community of Color series is more than just a series of books about colors. The series demonstrates how individual people, places, and things combine to form a community. It allows children to view the world in segments and then experience the wonderment and value of the community as a whole.

Orange as a pumpkin

Orange comme une citrouille

Orange leaves
on the ground

Orange comme
du feuillage à terre

Orange tangerines

Orange comme les tangerines

Orange cheese balls
in a mound.

Orange comme
les boules de fromage.

Orange as a cupcake

Orange comme
un petit gâteau

Orange flames in the fire

Orange comme les jolies flammes nues

Orange candy corn

Orange comme
les bonbons

Orange night-lights
on a wire.

Orange comme
les veilleuses suspendues.

Orange as a carrot

Orange comme une carotte

Orange mums by the pie

Orange comme
les chrysanthèmes

Orange harvest moon

Orange comme la lune au temps de la récolte

Orange balloons
floating by.

Orange comme des
ballons flottant sur l'air.

The color Orange
is all around.

On voit de
l'orange partout.

ABOUT COLOR

Use the Community of Color series to teach your child to identify the most basic colors and to help him or her relate these colors to objects in the real world. ASK:

- What color is this book about?
- Can you name the orange things at this party?
- How many orange pumpkins can you find?
- What orange fruit is in this picture?

ABOUT COMMUNITY

Use the Community of Color series to teach your child how he or she is an important part of the community. EXPLAIN TO YOUR CHILD WHAT A COMMUNITY IS.

- A community is a place where people live, work, and play together.
- Your family is a community.
- Your school is a community.
- Your neighborhood is a community.
- The world is one big community.

Everyone plays an important part in making a community work - moms, dads, boys, girls, police officers, firefighters, teachers, mail carriers, garbage collectors, store clerks, and even animals are all important parts of a community. USE THESE QUESTIONS TO FURTHER THE CONVERSATION:

- How are the people at this party interacting with one another?
- How are the people different from one another? How are they the same?
- What do they have in common?
- How is the community you see in this book like your community? How is it different?
- Describe your community.

ABOUT FEELINGS

Colors can describe as well as evoke different emotions. Encourage your child to describe the feelings that the color orange inspires.

- How does the color orange make you feel?
- Name your favorite orange thing in this book. Why is it your favorite?
- Name your favorite orange thing at home. Why is it your favorite?
- Can you tell how the people in the picture feel by looking at their faces? Do you ever feel the same way? When? Why?

TRY SOMETHING NEW . . . Brighten someone's day! Bring pumpkins to your local senior center. Help the residents decorate. (Make sure you ask an adult to help.)